ANTIRACIST BABY

To Imani, to all my Faith.
— I. X. K.

To all the young people whose own imaginations are unbound by
the imaginations of state violence and white supremacy, and who hold
the power to build a world that is antiracist. I believe in us.
— A.L.

PUFFIN BOOKS
Puffin Books is part of the Penguin Random House group of companies whose addresses
can be found at global.penguinrandomhouse.com

 Penguin Random House UK

First published in the United States of America by Kokila,
an imprint of Penguin Random House LLC, 2020
Published in Great Britain by Puffin Books 2021
Text copyright © Ibram X. Kendi, 2020
Cover art and illustrations copyright © Ashley Lukashevsky, 2020
The moral right of the author and illustrator has been asserted
Design by Jasmin Rubero • Text set in Aniara Regular with Gill Sans Regular
A CIP catalogue record for this book is available from the British Library

All correspondence to: Puffin Books, Penguin Random House Children's
One Embassy Gardens, 8 Viaduct Gardens, London SW11 7BW

The authorized representative in the EEA is Penguin Random House Ireland,
Morrison Chambers, 32 Nassau Street, Dublin D02 YH68

ISBN: 978–0–241–51238–8
Printed and bound in Italy • 001

We would like to acknowledge the contribution of the educators from #DisruptTexts
(Tricia Ebarvia, Lorena Germán, Kim Parker, and Julia E. Torres) in collaborating on the
discussion questions for parents and caregivers.
To review a full discussion guide by #DisruptTexts visit bit.ly/AntiracistBabyGuide

 MIX
Paper from
responsible sources
FSC® C018179

ANTIRACIST BABY

ILLUSTRATIONS BY

IBRAM X. KENDI **ASHLEY LUKASHEVSKY**

PUFFIN

Antiracist Baby is bred, *not* born.

Antiracist Baby is raised
to make society transform.

Babies are taught to be racist or antiracist – there's no neutrality.

Take these nine steps to make equity a reality.

Antiracist Baby learns all the colours,
not because race is true.
If you claim to be colour-blind,
you deny what's right in front of you.

No one will see racism if we only stay silent.
If we don't name racism,
it won't stop being so violent.

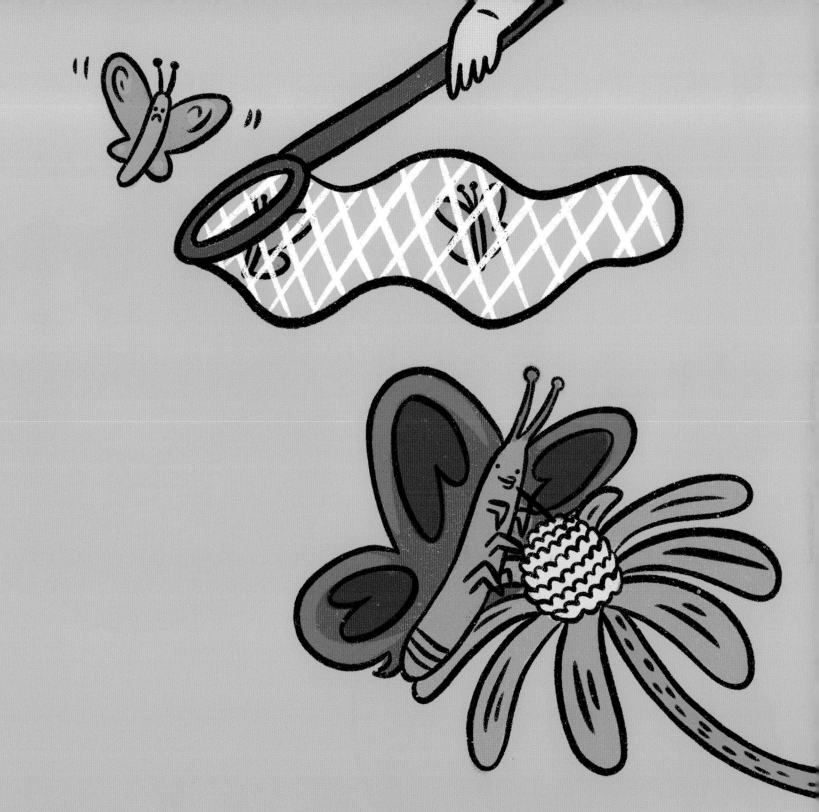

Some people get more, while others get less . . .
because policies don't always grant equal access.

4 Shout, "There's nothing wrong with the people!"

Even though all races are not treated the same,

"We are all human!" Antiracist Baby can proclaim.

Antiracist Baby doesn't see certain groups as "better" or "worse". Antiracist Baby loves a world that's truly diverse.

Antiracist Baby appreciates how groups speak, dance and create as they choose. Antiracist Baby welcomes all groups voicing their unique views.

7 Confess when being racist.

Nothing disrupts racism more than when we confess
the racist ideas that we sometimes express.

Antiracist Baby is always learning, changing and growing.

Antiracist Baby stays curious about all people and isn't all-knowing.

Antiracist Baby is filled with
the power to transcend, my friend.
And doesn't judge a book by its cover,
but reads until . . .

THE END.

Dear Parents and Caregivers,

It is critical that we begin explicit conversations about race and racism with our children from a young age. Just as we teach our kids to be kind even before they fully understand what it means to be kind, we should teach our kids to be antiracist even before they fully understand what it means to be antiracist. When we are afraid to talk about race, kids assume that it's a topic that they, too, are supposed to avoid. Since studies show that children are exposed to racist messages all around them in our society, it is our responsibility to counter those messages by helping children learn to be antiracist.

Here are some questions and discussion starters to encourage conversations about race and racism with young children.

Ask your child: "When you imagine a farmer, a teacher or an astronaut – what do they look like?"

You might find that kids default to white authority figures in their imaginations. Ask them about why this might be so. This could lead to conversations about how we must be conscientious and critical of the images we're presented in media. What is the effect of setting the default for authority figures to white?

Ask your child to describe the people in their friend group and yours.

It is a fallacy that children are "colour-blind". Help your child explicitly name the race of the people around them so they understand it is not insulting or harmful to do so. We want to normalize discussions about race and remove the stigma around these conversations.

It is important for children to name the race of the people around them so you can ask them what they think about those different races, why they think those things, and instruct them on how to understand racial difference – as an imagined construct, but one with very real consequences. You want to teach them this. You don't want to assume children are "blank slates" – this leaves room for racist societal messages to shape their understanding of racism instead.

Help children understand that racist policies are the problem, not people.

You and the child can reflect on the racial make-up of your school or neighbourhood. Are they truly diverse? Or do you live in a neighbourhood or attend a school made up mostly by people from a particular race? Help children understand that this is a result of racist policy, and talk about how this affects which schools may receive more resources over others. Or discuss how children who experience poverty, food insecurity or homelessness are disproportionately Black and brown. Ask the child why they think this may be the case and talk about the conditions that caused this, making clear it is not the fault of the Black or brown child or their parents.

Challenge the idea that all people are treated the same.

It is common to share lessons like "be kind to everyone" with kids, but this reinforces the idea that racist acts are only carried out on an individual level and ignores that all people are not given the same access to necessary resources. Although we might teach kids that "anyone can do anything", we also have to teach them that racist barriers exist that stop us all from being truly free. Understanding this is the first step in helping to change it. Being kind does not mean that we avoid seeing race, but that we celebrate racial differences.

Share your own experiences with racism.

The heartbeat of racism is denial. If you can model for a child that it is OK to confess our own racist beliefs and actions and how we are working to change them, they are less likely to be ashamed when we point out how they may have absorbed a message from society that is truly racist.

For example, if a child expresses that they think darker-skinned people are less beautiful than lighter-skinned people, you can perhaps share a time when you thought so, how and why you changed, and what you now know – that all of the skin colours are equally beautiful. Engage kids in discussion about how messaging in the stories, advertisements, and toys they see might have given

them this idea so they can recognize it, reject it, and form a new understanding without being held back by shame or embarrassment.

Remember to talk to your kids about how people aren't just "racist" or "antiracist", but rather how their actions can be racist or anti-racist.

Kids might understand how this is similar to when we say we don't consider them to be "a bad kid" when they do something wrong, but we must acknowledge that they made a bad choice. They have the opportunity to make a better choice the next time, because we know that identity is not fixed. Being antiracist is about what we do, not who we are. Being measured by our actions allows us to continue to grow.

– Ibram X. Kendi

Glossary

This book uses words that are complicated and which can be tricky to understand, so it is important that we define them clearly. Definitions anchor us in principles. If we don't do the basic work of defining the kind of people we want to be in language that is stable and consistent, we can't work towards stable, consistent goals.

Race A way of classifying different groups of people according to the colour of their skin. There are no meaningful scientific differences between people of different races, but identifying them has been useful historically to hold power over groups of people.

Racism Policies and actions that discriminate against or continue the disadvantages of a particular race.

Antiracism Fighting against racism by supporting policies through actions, or expressing ideas. People cannot be wholly "racist" or "antiracist": only their thoughts and actions can.

Society A group of people who depend upon each other, and who are subject to the same sets of rules. Society is made up of many different and varied people.

Neutrality Being in-between two things and not taking a side. We can't choose not to take a side when it comes to racism because simply being "not racist" will allow racism to continue.

Equity As opposed to equality, equity is the work of ensuring that two or more groups are given greater or lesser advantages, meaning that they can benefit equally from opportunities. Sometimes, to treat some people equally, we must treat them differently.

Equal Access Taking action to make sure that people from different groups are given the same opportunities, even when they have different backgrounds.

Policies Rules, principles and guidance established by organizations, governments or other powerful bodies. All policies are necessarily either racist or antiracist.

Further Reading

To find out more about some of the issues raised in this book, please take a look at **www.puffin.co.uk/antiracistbaby** which is full of extra resources for children, grown-ups, teachers and librarians.

And here is a selection of other useful resources and organizations you can find online:

BBC Bitesize
https://www.bbc.co.uk/bitesize/topics/z7rrd2p/resources/1

BLAM (Black Learning Achievement and Mental Health)
https://blamuk.org/our-guides-and-research/

Childline
https://www.childline.org.uk/info-advice/bullying-abuse-safety/crime-law/racism-racial-bullying

Embrace Race
https://www.embracerace.org/assets/embraceracetipsenglish-(2).pdf

NSPCC (National Society for the Prevention of Cruelty to Children)
https://www.nspcc.org.uk/globalassets/documents/race-and-racism/unicef-anti-racism-resource-pack.pdf

Race Conscious
http://www.raceconscious.org/2016/06/100-race-conscious-things-to-say-to-your-child-to-advance-racial-justice/

Red Cross
https://www.redcross.org.uk/get-involved/teaching-resources/talking-with-children-and-young-people-about-race-and-racism